What Shines?
¿Qué brilla?

by Deborah Schecter

ISBN: 978-1-338-70272-9
Illustrated by Anne Kennedy
Copyright © 2020 by Deborah Schecter. All rights reserved.
Published by Scholastic Inc., 557 Broadway, New York, NY 10012

10 9 8 7 6   68   23 24 25 26/0

Printed in Jiaxing, China. First printing, June 2020.

SCHOLASTIC

The sun shines.

El sol brilla.

A flashlight shines.

La linterna brilla.

The moon shines.

La luna brilla.

A dime shines.

La moneda brilla.

A ring shines.

El anillo brilla.

My shoes shine.

Mis zapatos brillan.

I shine!

¡Yo brillo!